Write your way to success with CGP!

*This CGP book is perfect for helping Year 5 pupils improve their writing —
it's packed with guided activities based on a wide range of styles and genres,
plus 'extra challenge' questions to get them writing independently.*

*Answers to every question are included in a cut-out-and-keep section,
so it's easy to keep track of how pupils are getting on.*

*You can also download free annotated examples of a range of text types
to give pupils ideas for their own writing. You'll find them here:*

www.cgpbooks.co.uk/KS2WritingResources

What CGP is all about

*Our sole aim here at CGP is to produce the highest quality books
— carefully written, immaculately presented and
dangerously close to being funny.*

*Then we work our socks off to get them out to you
— at the cheapest possible prices.*

Contents

The exercises in this book cover different types of writing, and different techniques you can use to make your writing effective. Use the contents below to see what's covered where.

Section 1 — Drafting Your Work

Planning Your Writing.....................3

Editing Your Work 6

Proofreading Your Work.................8

Section 2 — Writing Non-Fiction

Brilliant Bats 9
Non-chronological report — using headings, sub-headings and bullet points

A Day in the Life 12
Diary entry — writing in the first person, using the past and present tense

The Life of Galileo 15
Biography — ordering paragraphs, using linking words and phrases

Swans Storm School 18
Newspaper article — using relative clauses and noun phrases, varying sentence structures

Scrimshaw's Sensational Serum.................21
Advert — using persuasive techniques

Film of the Month 24
Review — writing for different audiences

Section 3 — Writing Fiction

The Haunted Hills 27
Ghost story — describing settings

The Wizard of Whitby 30
Fantasy — describing characters

Sherbet's Sweetshop...................33
Contemporary — writing effective openings

Whitebeard's Wrath......................36
Adventure — writing effective endings

A Lucky Escape........................39
Play script — using dialogue and stage directions to advance action

Answers.................................42

Glossary

Published by CGP

Editors: Claire Boulter, Andy Cashmore, Alex Fairer

Contributors: Samantha Bensted, Alison Griffin, Amanda MacNaughton, Maxine Petrie

With thanks to Catherine Heygate and Amanda MacNaughton for the proofreading.

With thanks to Emily Smith for the copyright research.

ISBN: 978 1 78294 956 5

Thumb illustration used throughout the book © iStock.com.

Images and clipart throughout the book from Corel® and clipart.com

Printed by Elanders Ltd, Newcastle upon Tyne.

Based on the classic CGP style created by Richard Parsons.

Planning Your Writing

Before you start writing, you need to plan your work — this includes thinking about the purpose and audience. The purpose and audience of your text affect the language you use — e.g. a letter to a friend might use informal language.

Planning also includes thinking about how to structure your writing — e.g. how to start and end your text, what order your ideas should come in.

Key Terms

- The <u>purpose</u> of a text is the reason why it's been written.
- e.g. a story to entertain readers

- The <u>audience</u> is the person or people who the text is aimed at.
- e.g. a magazine article for teenagers, a letter to your headteacher

1 Circle the correct purpose and audience for each writing idea in the table.

Writing Idea	Purpose	Audience
1. A story about a talking teddy bear that is trying to find its way home.	Advise / Entertain	Children / Teenagers
2. An article from a local newspaper weighing up whether to ban cars from parking in the city centre.	Discuss / Inform	Children / Adults
3. A leaflet from a secondary school tennis club saying why students should go to a taster session.	Explain / Persuade	Adults / Teenagers

Write the number of the writing idea next to the language style it should be written in.

Formal, factual language ....

Simple, descriptive language ....

Personal, convincing language ....

2 **Read this plan for a story set in space.**

1. Woman is attacked by aliens.

2. Woman goes into space.

3. Woman crashes her spaceship.

4. Woman defeats aliens.

5. Woman fixes her spaceship.

6. Woman goes home.

> Try writing these parts out and cutting them into strips to help you rearrange them.

Plan three different stories by rearranging the parts of the plan.

1. ....

2. ....

3. ....

> Just write the numbers, not the full points.

⭐ **Extra Challenge**

How many different plans can you come up with in two minutes using these points? Make sure each plan works.

3 **Fill in the gaps to complete the plan for an adventure story. You can use the picture and the hints to help you.**

1. Beginning — ....

2. Omar finds a waterfall in the jungle.

3. Omar takes ....

4. The Queen of the Jungle sees Omar leaving the waterfall.

5. Omar and the Queen of the Jungle ....

6. End — ....

> Why is Omar in the jungle?

> What does Omar take from the waterfall?

> Is the Queen happy or unhappy that Omar took something?

> What happens at the end?

4 Below are topics to go into a report about Japan. Circle two topics that should go in the introduction. Underline two topics that should go in the conclusion.

- Where Japan is in the world
- Anime — Japanese cartoons
- Japan under the Samurai
- The future of Japan

- Sushi and other Japanese food
- Name of Japan's capital city
- How the reader could learn more
- Shrines and religion

Circle the correct option from each pair to choose the most appropriate language style for this report.

First person uses words like 'I' and 'me'. Third person uses words like 'he', 'she' and 'it'.

Formal / Informal

Factual / Descriptive

First Person / Third Person

 5 Below is the plan for a diary entry about a family day out at the seaside. Complete the plan by writing what the middle of the diary entry will include.

Introduction — Describe my excitement on the car journey.

Think of three things you might do at the seaside.

Write in the first person (using 'I' and 'me').

Paragraph 1 — ....
....

Paragraph 2 — ....
....

Paragraph 3 — ....
....

Conclusion — How I fell asleep on the journey home.

★ **Extra Challenge**

Plan a diary entry about something fun that you did recently.

"I can plan fiction and non-fiction texts."

Editing Your Work

Every piece of writing you do needs to be edited. This means reading it carefully to check whether it's suitable for the audience and purpose, how well it flows and whether it makes sense.

It's also a chance to make it better in other ways — for example, by choosing more interesting words or adding suspense.

> Reading your work aloud can help you see how it could be improved.

1 These are extracts from the first draft of a report about curling. For each part, draw a line to the editing change that will make the extract better.

1. Curling is a game played on ice where teams push rounded stones down a lane towards a target, aiming for its centre to win points.

2. There are two teams. Each team has four players. They take it in turns to slide stones.

3. Each team has eight round stones which are smooth and round. They can be used to hit the opponent's eight round stones.

> Combine sentences to help the text flow.

> Remove extra words.

> Split sentences so they are easier to read.

Rewrite each extract with the changes it needs.

> You can change the text in other ways too if you want.

1. ....

....

2. ....

....

....

3. ....

....

....

(2) The writing in black is the start of a mystery story. Write on it any changes that would make it better, such as splitting up or combining sentences, or using more interesting words.

The first two changes have been marked on in red.

Use a more interesting verb.   Add more description of the setting.

Detective Juan <u>looked</u> around the <u>crime scene</u>.

He looked at the safe that was wide open.

Inside the safe was a handwritten note. The note read that the thief had struck again, and that Detective Juan's pet poodle was next, but Detective Juan was not scared or terrified and he pulled out his magnifying glass to look around the crime scene for clues.

★ **Extra Challenge**
Write a second draft of this extract based on the changes you have suggested.

(3) This is an extract from a newspaper article. Write on it any changes that would make it better.

Hamster Recovers Keys to Hardware Shop

A hamster named Nora made the news yesterday.

Nora, a grey and white hamster, stopped disaster yesterday by getting the key to a hardware shop which had accidentally been locked inside by staff.

The grey and white hamster tunnelled inside through an unused pipe. She found the keys on the kitchen floor. She then came back outside.

★ **Extra Challenge**
Write a second draft of this extract. Swap it with a friend and suggest changes to each other's work.

"I can edit my work to make it better."

Section 1 — Drafting Your Work

8

Proofreading Your Work

When you've finished editing your writing, you should proofread it.
This means looking for mistakes in spelling, punctuation and grammar,
as well as any incorrect facts or places where the writing isn't clear.

1 This is a late draft of the beginning of a story set in the wild west.
Read it carefully. Circle each mistake and write the correction above it.

It was tuff being the sheriff of Hisstown. For the start, Natalia hated

the snakes that lurked in the grass outside of town. the bright green snakes

was easy to spot when they slithered into town, but the pale yellow ones were

sneakier. Natalia has found one in her bed once. She slept outside four three

nights before the snake left. The memory made her shudder.

What really made being the sheriff hard was Ryans gang of bandits.

They'd had held up coaches, burgled wealfy landowners and stolen bread from

bakery countless times. Annoyingly, Natalia couldn't find there hideout.

As natalia gazed across the fields in the warm glow of the rising son, her

deputy, Franklin, came running.

"Sheriff, I've have great news,"

he said. "I no where the hideout is."

Excellent! Natalia exclaimed.

"Let's get going right away"!

"I can proofread my work and correct mistakes."

Brilliant Bats

When you write a non-fiction text, it should be clear and easy to follow.

Layout features such as headings, subheadings and bullet points can make your writing easier to understand.

Key Terms

- <u>Headings</u> tell the reader the main topic of the text.

  e.g. 'Super Snails' could be the heading of a text about snails.

- <u>Subheadings</u> divide up the text into smaller sections.

  e.g. 'Slow movers' could be the subheading of a section about how snails move.

- <u>Bullet points</u> separate the information in a list.

  e.g. Snails usually eat:

  - leaves   · plant stems   · bark

---

1 This is an extract from a report about bats. Label the layout features.

<u>Brilliant Bats</u> ← [_____]

Many Different Varieties

It is believed that more than 1000 species of bat exist today.

All Over the World ← [_____]

The only places in the world where bats do not live are:

- The Arctic   · The Antarctic   · Some islands ← [_____]

Explain how each of these layout features makes the text easier to follow.

Layout feature	How it makes the text easier to follow
Subheadings	
Bullet points	

2 These are extracts from later in the report. Write a subheading for each one.

....

Most bats eat

insects. Others eat

fruit, fish and frogs.

....

Bats generally live in

sheltered places such

as caves and barns.

....

Bats often sleep

upside down,

hanging by their toes.

3 Rewrite the text below, using bullet points to break it up.

Today, bats all over the world are at risk. This is due to a number of factors, such as destruction of their habitat, reduced food supply and disease. You can help bats by putting up boxes in your garden for them to sleep in, growing plants which will attract insects for them to eat and joining a bat conservation group.

....

> Look out for lists that could be turned into bullet points.

....

....

....

....

....

....

....

....

....

4 This is an extract from a report about owls. Rewrite the text with a heading, subheadings and bullet points.

Think about how best to split the text into sections.

Britain is home to at least five species of owl, including the Little Owl, the Tawny Owl and the Barn Owl. Owls have excellent eyesight and sharp talons, which make them very effective predators. Catching a glimpse of an owl is tricky. They usually fly at night, and are silent and well camouflaged.

....

....

....

....

....

....

....

....

....

....

....

★ **Extra Challenge**

Write a short report about your favourite animal. Include a heading, subheadings and bullet points.

"I can organise my writing using layout features."

A Day in the Life

When you write about things that happened or are happening to you, you should write in the first person to get across your thoughts and feelings.

It is also important to use the past and present tenses consistently so the time frame of events is clear to the reader.

Key Terms

- The <u>first person</u> is used to write from the point of view of the writer.

    e.g. 'I love my pet goldfish.'

- The <u>past tense</u> is used to write about things that have already happened.

    e.g. 'I won a race yesterday morning.'

- The <u>present tense</u> is used to write about things that are happening now.

    e.g. 'I feel very proud of myself.'

(1) This extract is from a diary entry about a school day. Underline the words in the extract that tell you it is written in the first person.

I woke up this morning with a feeling of dread. Our teacher had asked everyone

in the class to give a presentation. We had each been given a topic; mine was

penguins. I hate giving presentations and birds are my least favourite kind of

animal. Feeling sorry for myself, I trudged downstairs.

> Think about how the extract would come across if it used 'he' or 'she' instead. Would it seems more or less personal?

(2) Read the next part of the diary entry. Fill in the gaps so that the extract is written in the first person.

After breakfast, ... set out for school alone, the nerves already building

up inside .... As I walked through the park, I tried to comfort ....

with the thought that .... friend's presentation was about slugs. Surely

.... would be more interesting than that. However, ... thoughts

were suddenly interrupted by the astonishing sight of a penguin near the swings.

(3) Circle the correct options from the words in bold so that this extract from the diary uses tenses correctly.

> Think about how using the wrong tense might affect the reader.

I stood **stared / staring** at the penguin as it happily **waddled / waddles** around. I was about to **ring / rang** my mum when I spotted a zookeeper **entered / entering** the park. I **run / ran** over and told him that I had found a penguin. He said he **had been / has been** searching for it for several hours.

(4) There are some mistakes in the tenses in the final extract from the diary entry. Circle the errors.

The zookeeper is incredibly grateful to me for finding the penguin. I tell him about my presentation and he gives me some fascinating penguin facts. I thanked him and continue walking to school. When I delivered my presentation, I have so much to talk about that I don't felt nervous at all. On reflection, I am pleased with how it goes. I still couldn't believe what happened!

Rewrite the extract so that it uses tenses correctly.

> Make it clear that these events happened in the past.

....

....

....

....

....

....

....

5 Write a diary entry about an interesting day from your own life. Write in the first person to make your writing personal. Make sure you use tenses correctly so your writing is clear. You can use the picture and hints below to help you.

You could write about a holiday, a day out somewhere or something fun you did with friends.

Write about who you were with, what you did and how you felt about it.

Don't forget to mention when the events happened and where you were.

You could mention how you feel now — remember to use the present tense.

....

....

....

....

....

....

....

....

....

....

....

"I can write in the first person and use tenses correctly."

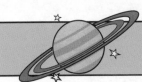 

The Life of Galileo

You can make your writing clear by ordering paragraphs so they flow logically.

To make your writing easier to read, you should link your sentences and paragraphs together — you can do this using words and phrases that show the order things happened in, as well as the cause and effect of events.

Key Terms

- <u>Paragraphs</u> are sections of writing that focus on a particular theme. You start a new paragraph when you start writing about a new time, place or topic.

e.g. Richard III died in 1485 at the Battle of Bosworth Field.
     Next came Henry VII...

- <u>Linking words and phrases</u> join together clauses, sentences and paragraphs.

e.g. Sinatra was a singer and he acted. As a result, he became famous.

1 These are the topics to be included in a biography of Galileo Galilei. Write the topics in a sensible order on the lines below.

- Galileo's education
- Galileo's early life
- Discoveries about space (1609-1617)

- Galileo's death
- Physics experiments (1638)
- Placed under house arrest by the Church (1633)

Think about what order would make the text easiest to follow.

1. ....

2. ....

3. ....

4. ....

5. ....

6. ....

2 This is the start of the biography. Circle the correct option from the linking words in bold to make the writing flow.

Galileo Galilei was born in 1564 in Italy.

Rarely / Initially, the Galilei family lived in Pisa.

Therefore / However, in 1574 they moved to Florence.

Galileo's father, Vincenzo Galilei, was a famous lute

player. **Because of this / In contrast**, Galileo became

skilled in the instrument too. **Although / Since**

Vincenzo had to work hard to support his family, he

found time to tutor Galileo in Latin and Greek.

3 The sentence below is the end of a paragraph. Use the information in the box to write the next paragraph. Start it with a suitable linking word or phrase, and use linking words or phrases to join sentences and clauses in your paragraph.

Despite Galileo's early desire to become a priest, he followed his father's wishes and decided to train as a doctor.

....

....

....

....

....

....

....

- In 1581, Galileo began a medical degree.
- At university, he attended a maths lecture.
- He became fascinated by maths.
- His maths teacher asked Galileo's father to let him study maths instead of medicine.

4 Below are some events that relate to Galileo's discoveries about the solar system. Write two paragraphs summarising these events.

- Galileo built one of the first ever telescopes (1609).

- Galileo discovered that Venus appeared to change shape. From this, he concluded that the Sun was the centre of the solar system (1610).

- Church ruled that Earth was the centre of the solar system (1616).

- Galileo released a book stating that the Church's theory about the solar system was wrong (1632).

- Church put Galileo on trial. He was put under house arrest for the rest of his life (1633).

Think about which events should come in which paragraph.

Link sentences and paragraphs together with linking words and phrases.

....

....

....

....

....

....

....

....

....

....

....

★ **Extra Challenge**

Write a short biography of someone famous. Order your paragraphs in a way that makes sense and use linking words and phrases.

"I can order paragraphs logically and link ideas to make my writing flow."

Section 2 — Writing Non-Fiction

Swans Storm School

You can make your writing more interesting and informative by adding relative clauses and noun phrases to sentences to give the reader extra information.

Varying the structure of your sentences can also help to make your writing more interesting.

Grammar Guide

- A <u>clause</u> is part of a sentence that has a verb and someone doing the action.

  e.g. Jo cleaned the socks

- <u>Relative clauses</u> give extra information about a noun. They often start with who, that or which.

  e.g. the socks, which Lily had knitted, were warm

- A <u>noun phrase</u> contains a noun and any words that describe the noun. Noun phrases can be expanded by adding extra detail.

  e.g. the socks is a noun phrase

  e.g. the purple socks with the hole is an expanded noun phrase

> Relative clauses can be separated from the rest of the sentence by commas or brackets.

1 This is an extract from a newspaper report. Fill each gap with a relative clause to give the reader extra information about the noun in bold.

Pupils and staff at Lastanthem Primary School in Wattleton were left

stunned yesterday after ten swans charged into the school's kitchen and

gobbled up the **food** that ....

The bevy of **swans**, who ....,

squeezed through a **hole** in the playground fence which ....

....

The swans then dashed to the kitchen

where they devoured the **pizzas** that

....

....

2 Rewrite each sentence below, expanding the underlined noun phrases.

Cafeteria staff told reporters what happened.

....

....

The swans stormed the kitchen.

....

....

Two of the swans kept guard while the others took the pizzas.

....

....

> Noun phrases give extra information about nouns — they often include adjectives.

3 For each box below, write two different sentences by arranging the sentence parts in different orders.

> Add capital letters and punctuation where they are needed.

- within ten minutes of the swan invasion
- the chef sneaked out of the kitchen

1. ....

2. ....

- the chef alerted the headteacher
- after sprinting across the playground

> How does changing the order of the sentence parts affect the main focus of each sentence?

1. ....

2. ....

....

★ Extra Challenge

Come up with two more sentence parts that can be arranged in different ways to form a sentence for the report.

Section 2 — Writing Non-Fiction

4 Continue the newspaper report, explaining how the swans were removed from the kitchen. Use noun phrases and relative clauses to add information to your writing. Vary the structure of your sentences to make them interesting.

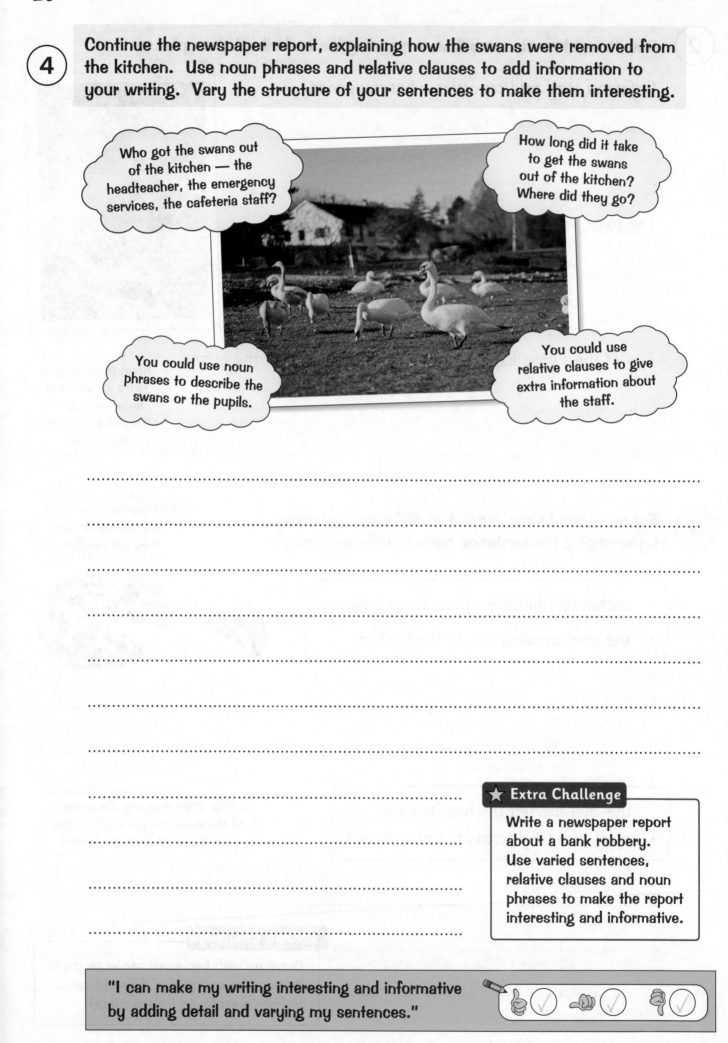

Who got the swans out of the kitchen — the headteacher, the emergency services, the cafeteria staff?

How long did it take to get the swans out of the kitchen? Where did they go?

You could use noun phrases to describe the swans or the pupils.

You could use relative clauses to give extra information about the staff.

....

....

....

....

....

....

....

....

⭐ **Extra Challenge**

Write a newspaper report about a bank robbery. Use varied sentences, relative clauses and noun phrases to make the report interesting and informative.

....

....

"I can make my writing interesting and informative by adding detail and varying my sentences."

Scrimshaw's Sensational Serum

Persuasive **writing aims to** convince **the reader** to do something, **or to agree with a point of view.** It is often used in adverts to make people buy products.

You can use techniques such as repetition, lists of three, rhetorical questions **and** exaggeration **to make your writing persuasive.**

Key Terms

<u>Repetition</u> is when certain words or phrases are used more than once.

e.g. Pizza scissors are a great product and a great addition to your kitchen.

A <u>list of three</u> is the use of three words or phrases to describe something.

e.g. Pizza scissors are practical, easy to use and great value.

<u>Rhetorical questions</u> are questions that don't need an answer.

e.g. Do you want to be able to cut pizza safely and easily?

<u>Exaggeration</u> is making something sound better or worse than it actually is.

e.g. Pizza scissors are the best thing you will ever buy.

(1) **This is an extract from an advert. Read the extract, then fill in the table below.**

Scrimshaw's Sensational Serum will make you whatever age you want for precisely one day. Scrimshaw's is safe to use, effortless to apply and brimming with possibilities. Do you long to relive your youth? Or know how it feels to be 80? Scrimshaw's can fulfil your every dream!

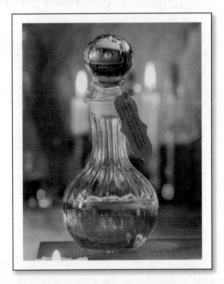

Technique	Example from the extract	Effect of the technique
List of three		
Rhetorical question		

Section 2 — Writing Non-Fiction

2 These are more sentences from the advert. Rewrite each one using the technique in brackets to make it more persuasive.

Think about how to make people want to buy the serum.

It is an ideal gift for anyone. (List of three)

....

The serum is selling out quickly. (Exaggeration)

....

You can be any age you want. (Repetition)

....

3 Read the rest of the advert below, then rewrite it to make it more persuasive.

You could repeat an important point.

Using Scrimshaw's Serum is a good experience.

It will give you a break from your ordinary

life. If you want to try being a different age,

then you should buy Scrimshaw's Serum now.

You could exaggerate the serum's qualities.

It is a good product at a fair price.

You could use a list of three positive adjectives.

....

....

....

....

....

....

....

4 Scrimshaw's has a new product — Scrimshaw's Super Socks. Write an advert persuading people to buy these socks. Use repetition, lists of three, rhetorical questions and exaggeration to make the advert as persuasive as possible.

Think about what special properties the socks might have, e.g. they could allow you to walk silently or to run really fast.

You could use rhetorical questions to make readers think about how comfy the socks are.

You could use exaggeration to highlight what good presents the socks would make.

You could use a list of three to emphasise the range of styles.

....

....

....

....

....

....

....

....

....

....

⭐ **Extra Challenge**

Write an advert for your favourite food using persuasive techniques.

"I can use a range of persuasive writing techniques." 👍 ✓ 👎 ✓ 👎 ✓

Section 2 — Writing Non-Fiction

Film of the Month

Writers vary their writing style depending on their audience — the person or people the writing is aimed at.

There's more about writing for an audience on p. 3.

When writing for adults, you might use complex words and longer sentences. When writing for children, you might use simpler words and shorter sentences.

1 These are extracts from two reviews of the same film. Draw a line from each extract to the audience it is aimed at.

Trish Lolam's latest comedy hit, 'Hole in None', brings to mind her superb debut, which won awards in 1993.

Children

Do you enjoy comedy films filled with jolly jokes and silly stunts? Then you will love 'Hole in None'!

Adults

2 Circle the correct options from the words in bold to make the film review extract suitable for children.

Think about what makes writing suitable for children.

Golf comedies are rare, but 'Hole in None' is the

funniest / most laughter-inducing film in years.

The plot is **really good / masterful**: Reuben, a

former golf caddy, is **in financial difficulties**

/ short of money when he hears about a golf

tournament with a **generous / big** cash prize.

Hilarity ensues / Things turn funny when he

tees off against the golfer he caddied for before their ugly falling out.

3 These sentences from a review of the same film are aimed at adults. Rewrite the sentences so they are suitable for children — use simpler language and split up the sentences.

Use a dictionary for any words you don't know.

The screenwriter creates hilarious dialogue, including the sarcastic insults and witty responses of the two main characters.

....

....

Bryan Penholds, the actor who portrays Reuben, has been nominated for numerous acting accolades.

....

....

4 Below is an extract from a review of the same film. Underline the words and phrases that show it is aimed at children, then rewrite it for an adult audience.

The coolest part of the film was the golf buggy chase at the end. The super-fast music as the good guy weaved past golfers at top speed was fab. The stuntman was awesome, which made the scene extra funny.

You could use a thesaurus to help find suitable words.

Join sentences together — use linking words so they flow.

....

....

....

....

Section 2 — Writing Non-Fiction

5 Write a review of a book you read recently for a website aimed at either children or adults. Use suitable language and sentence lengths for your audience.

What was the book about? You could start with a brief summary of the plot.

Give reasons for your opinions about the book.

Think about how to structure your review — you could discuss the things you liked, then any bits you didn't.

Use clear, straightforward language if you're writing for children and complex language if you're writing for adults.

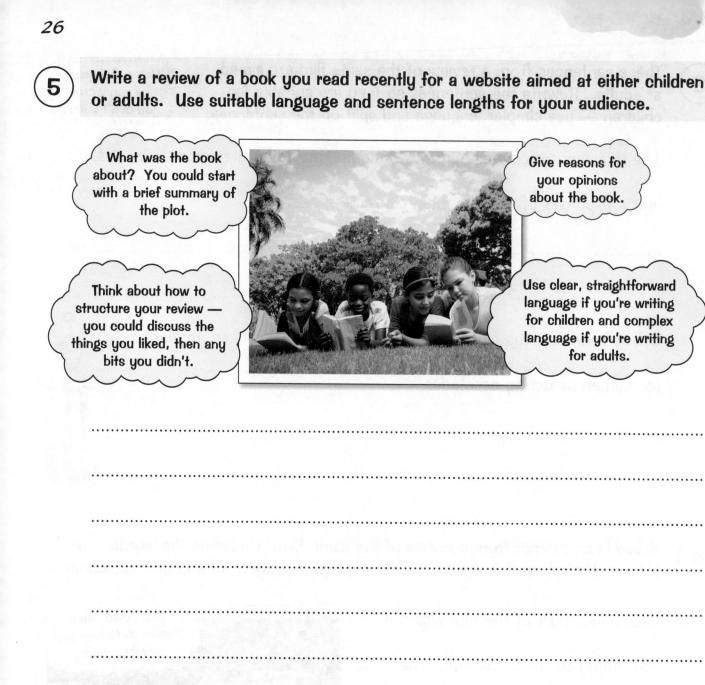

....

....

....

....

....

....

....

....

....

★ **Extra Challenge**

Rewrite your book review for the audience you didn't choose initially. Think about which words and sentences you need to change.

....

....

"I can adapt my writing for different audiences."

The Haunted Hills

Writers need to describe the settings in their stories effectively so readers can picture the places where the story's action is happening.

You can use similes, metaphors and personification to make your settings lifelike and memorable. Language which appeals to the senses can also help to make your writing vivid.

Key Terms

- A <u>simile</u> describes one thing as being similar to another.

  e.g. The bark of the tree looked like wrinkled skin.

- A <u>metaphor</u> describes something by saying it is something else.

  e.g. The tree was a mountain, timeless and unmovable.

- <u>Personification</u> uses human qualities to describe something that's not human.

  e.g. The tree's branches trembled anxiously in the strong wind.

- <u>Appeals to the senses</u> are descriptions of sight, sound, touch, taste or smell.

  e.g. The young leaves were soft and slightly damp between my fingers.

Similes often use the words 'like' or 'as'. Metaphors don't.

(1) **Below is an extract from a ghost story about a walker. Read the extract and fill in the table below.**

The wind was a million glass shards cutting through my clothes as I reached the top of the peak. All around me, rugged mountains stood guard over the land. On a nearby hill, the ruins of a castle sat like a row of jagged teeth. For a second, I saw a ghostly vision of the original castle standing there proudly, before a fluttering veil of mist obscured it.

Example	Technique used	How it makes you feel
The wind was a million glass shards		
the ruins of a castle sat like a row of jagged teeth		

2 The sentence in bold describes the walker's realisation that the weather is about to worsen. Rewrite it using a simile, then a metaphor, then personification.

In the distance, I spotted dark clouds.

Think about how to describe the clouds — do you want them to seem threatening or gentle?

Simile ....

Metaphor ....

Personification ....

3 The walker sees somewhere to shelter in the valley. Read the extract and underline the appeals to the senses.

Think about how the appeals to the senses make you feel.

I walked towards the stone hut, biting into a jam sandwich and savouring its tangy sweetness. I was almost there when a strong smell of smoke reached my nostrils. There was no-one around, but then I heard a deep, echoing horn and the heavy march of feet. Running to the hut, I thrust open the rotting wooden door, which was cold and clammy to the touch.

4 The walker waits in the hut for the weather to improve. Rewrite each sentence with a description that appeals to the sense given in brackets.

The hut was old and damp. (smell)

....

I sat on the stone floor. (touch)

....

Outside, a thunderstorm began. (sound)

....

(5) The walker hears the sounds of a battle and goes outside to see a ghostly army attacking the castle. Write a description of the setting.

> Write from the point of view of the walker, using 'I' and 'me'.

> What can the walker see of the landscape? You could use similes to describe it.

> What's the weather like? You could use metaphors to describe it.

> What does the castle look like? You could use personification to make it seem scary.

> What are the smells and the sounds of the battle? How might you appeal to the senses?

....

....

....

....

....

....

....

....

....

....

....

⭐ **Extra Challenge**

Write the next part of the story, focusing on describing the setting. You could describe the scene when the walker wakes up the next morning.

"I can describe settings effectively."

The Wizard of Whitby

When you are writing a story, you need to describe the characters effectively so readers can picture them clearly and get to know what they're like.

To create lifelike characters, you can use similes and metaphors. Language which appeals to the senses (sight, hearing, touch, taste and smell) can also help to create a vivid image of your characters.

See p.27 for more on these techniques.

 1 This is an extract from a fantasy story about a wizard. Underline the similes and circle the metaphors.

Wilbert's feet were heavy weights as he trudged inside and removed his hat and cloak. His eyes were usually twinkling stars, but now they were like dull, grey pools. Yet again, he'd had no new spells to show off at the annual wizarding conference. He felt as useless as a paper umbrella.

Choose one metaphor or simile and explain what it shows about Wilbert.

....

....

2 Fill in each gap using a simile or a metaphor to create a vivid image of Wilbert.

Wilbert was old. His lined face was .... and he

moved as .... as .... Achieving something

unique with his magic was his desire, something that people would remember,

but he felt his powers slipping away like ....

3 Draw a line from each of these sentences to the sense it appeals to.

Wilbert wrinkled his nose at the burnt stench
of a failed spell from the night before.

Smell

He smoothed the coarse, wiry hairs
of his long beard absent-mindedly.

Taste

He took a soothing sip of strong tea.

Touch

Explain how one of these appeals to the senses makes you feel.

....

4 Fill in each gap with an appeal to the senses to vividly describe Wilbert and his owl.

Wilbert felt .... tears trickling down his

Think about how you want the characters to come across.

cheeks and brushed them away. He heaved himself out of his

chair, his joints .... with the effort, and trudged towards

his bedroom. As he passed his owl, she gave a .... and

nestled close to him. Wilbert breathed in her .... scent.

5 Rewrite the extract below to create a vivid image of Wilbert and what he's doing.

Wilbert pulled his blanket around himself and fell asleep. His gentle snores grew

louder. At a sudden noise from outside, he opened his eyes and looked around.

Use similes, metaphors and appeals to the senses.

....

....

....

....

6 From his window, Wilbert sees a ship in trouble on the rocks. He performs an impressive spell to save the ship and its crew. Write a description of Wilbert as he does this. Use similes, metaphors and appeals to the senses.

> How does Wilbert feel when he first sees the ship? You could use similes to describe his feelings.

> What does Wilbert do? Use metaphors to describe how he moves and speaks.

> What does Wilbert sound like when he casts the spell? Appeal to the reader's sense of hearing.

> How does Wilbert behave after he has saved the ship?

....
....
....
....
....
....
....
....
....

★ **Extra Challenge**

Choose a friend or family member. Write a description of them that uses similes, metaphors and language that appeals to the senses.

"I can describe characters effectively."

 # Sherbet's Sweetshop

Having an effective beginning to a story makes the reader want to keep reading.

You can begin your stories with description to set the scene, or you can dive straight into the action to make the opening exciting. In an action-packed opening, you can use a rhetorical question to introduce a problem or puzzle.

Key Terms

- <u>Descriptive openings</u> create a vivid picture in your head. They use interesting adjectives and descriptive techniques.

  e.g. It was a gloomy, gusty night. The ghostly moon cast shadows like writhing snakes across the lawn.

- <u>Action-packed openings</u> jump straight into the events of the story. They often use powerful verbs and adverbs.

  e.g. Felipe leapt across the stream. He landed awkwardly, but sprinted onwards.

- A <u>rhetorical question</u> is a question where an answer isn't expected.

  e.g. Pia lost sight of the man in the street. How would she get her watch back now?

 Descriptive techniques can be found on p. 27

1 This is a descriptive opening to a story set in a sweetshop. Fill in the gaps with interesting descriptions to create a vivid picture of where the story is set.

Think about how you want the sweetshop to come across, e.g. you could make it sound appealing.

Sherbet's Sweetshop had stood in the same

spot, ...,

for as long as anyone could remember. The

walls were ....,

and the wooden door looked as though

.... In the window, racks of ....

chocolates jostled for space with .... Every

afternoon, dozens of .... children gathered outside,

.... and wondering what to buy.

2 This is a descriptive opening to a different story set in the same shop. Rewrite the extract with more interesting description so it is easier to picture where the story is set.

You could use interesting adjectives, similes and metaphors.

Hilda Sherbet gazed around her shop at all the sweets. She could hear children talking and laughing as they filled paper bags with different types of sweets.

She took a peppermint from one of the jars and ate it.

....

....

....

....

....

3 This is an action-packed opening to a story set in the sweetshop. Circle the verbs and adverbs in bold that create an exciting opening.

Think about which words are most dramatic.

Hilda **browsed / rummaged** through her filing cabinet, **tossing / lowering** papers **frantically / methodically** behind her onto the wooden floor. Nothing! She

sauntered / dashed to the front of the shop and **shoved / lifted** aside trays of brightly coloured sweets, peering **serenely / desperately** underneath them. Still nothing!

Write a rhetorical question to introduce a problem to this opening.

What question might the reader want answering?

....

4 This is the start of a plot outline for another story set in the sweetshop. Write an action-packed opening using this outline.

> Use interesting verbs and adverbs. You could use a rhetorical question.

Hilda arrives at the shop, eager to try a new recipe, but she's locked out.

....

....

....

....

....

5 Write the opening of a story based on the picture of a toyshop below.

> You could get straight into the action by having something happen to someone in the shop or to the toys.

> You could set the scene by describing the toyshop or the different toys for sale.

> You could use a rhetorical question to introduce a problem.

> You could describe an interesting character in the shop, e.g. a customer.

....

....

....

....

....

....

> ★ **Extra Challenge**
>
> Choose your favourite book. Rewrite its opening in a different way (e.g. if it's descriptive, make it action-packed).

"I can begin stories effectively."

Whitebeard's Wrath

Stories can end in different ways — endings can be happy or sad.

You can write a clear-cut ending that resolves the story's main problem or dilemma, or an open ending which leaves the reader guessing. Endings can also have a twist to surprise the reader.

Key Terms

A <u>clear-cut ending</u> resolves the main problem or dilemma of a story.

e.g. Sam held his breath and cut the wire. The bomb stopped ticking. The world was saved.

An <u>open ending</u> leaves the reader to imagine what happens next.

e.g. Sam held the clippers. Which wire to cut? He shut his eyes and snipped one.

A <u>twist ending</u> finishes a story with an unexpected outcome.

e.g. Sam clipped the wire. The bomb stopped ticking. He had finished the game.

1 Below are two different endings to an adventure story. Draw lines between each ending and the descriptions that best match it.

"Now I rule the seven seas," Whitebeard cackled, waving the golden monkey medallion.

Amy drew her cutlass and leapt at the pirate, who cursed and swung at her with his vicious hook. Amy was too quick; she darted behind Whitebeard and, with a shove, sent him staggering towards the side of the ship. As he tried to regain his balance, she snatched her father's precious medallion from the pirate's grimy hand. With a swift kick, she propelled him overboard, where he could do no more harm.

Clear-cut

Open

"Now I rule the seven seas," Whitebeard cackled, waving the golden monkey medallion.

Her hands bound by ropes, Amy stepped slowly along the wobbling plank. Her eyes welled with tears as she saw her father's prized possession clutched in Whitebeard's grimy hand. With a sneer, he poked Amy with a splintered oar. Teetering at the end of the plank, Amy stared into the swirling sea below.

Sad

Happy

Why might you choose to end your writing in each of these ways?

2 Tick the box next to the open ending and then finish the ending you ticked.

Amy and Whitebeard grab the medallion, but it's not clear who gets it. ☐

Amy gets the medallion and Whitebeard is never seen again. ☐

Whitebeard keeps the medallion and rules over the seas forever. ☐

What happens next? Does Amy fight Whitebeard?

Whitebeard waved the medallion triumphantly.

Suddenly, the ship lurched as a wave struck it.

....

....

....

....

....

How can you keep the ending open?

....

....

Think about how this ending might make the reader feel. Why might writers use open endings?

3 This is the start of a different ending to the same story. Finish the ending by writing a twist.

Your ending should surprise the reader.

"With your father's medallion, I'll rule the seven seas forever," Whitebeard

cackled, thrusting his trophy aloft triumphantly.

....

....

....

....

Section 3 — Writing Fiction

4 In a different adventure story, Amy and her rival Short Jack Bronze race to find a mythical treasure. Use the picture below to write the ending to this story. Decide what type of ending you want the story to have before you start writing.

Is it going to be a happy or sad ending?

You could make the ending open by leaving the reader to imagine what happens next.

You could write a clear-cut ending by making it clear who gets the treasure.

Is there a twist at the end of the story?

Amy sprinted up the pebbly beach to the cave where the treasure lay, with

Short Jack Bronze close upon her heels. ....

....

....

....

....

....

....

....

....

....

> ★ **Extra Challenge**
>
> Write a different type of ending to this story. For example, if you wrote an open ending, you could write an ending with a twist.

"I can write effective endings for my stories."

A Lucky Escape

You can show the action of a story through dialogue instead of describing what's happening. This can move the story forward and make your writing more interesting and exciting for the reader.

In a script, you can use dialogue to make it clearer what a character is doing and why. You can also use stage directions to show action in a script.

Key Terms

A script is used for plays and films. It is made up of dialogue and stage directions. Character names on the left show who is speaking.

e.g. (TREVOR picks up a cake.)
TREVOR: This cake looks delicious.

Dialogue is what a character says.

e.g. TREVOR: No-one will know if I eat it.

Stage directions show how dialogue is said and what characters are doing.

e.g. (TREVOR slumps on a chair.)
TREVOR: (Unhappily) I feel a bit sick.

1 This is the beginning of a play script. Underline the dialogue that shows action.

(ZARA carries a bag of tools into the hideout. CHARLIE follows her.)

ZARA: Ah! These tools are too heavy. They're falling out of my hands.

CHARLIE: Stop whining. Give them here — I'll put them on the table.

ZARA: Thanks. I'll get the floor plans — we need to know the mansion's layout.

CHARLIE: Can we do it later? I'm going to get a snack first. (Exits.)

ZARA: Are you kidding? Fine, I'll make notes on how to get the emerald myself.

How would the extract come across to the reader if all the action was given in stage directions? Would it be more or less interesting?

★ Extra Challenge

Write the next part of the script, in which Charlie comes back in and Zara explains what she's doing. Use dialogue to show what's happening.

2 **This is a later part of the play. Continue the scene, using dialogue to show action.**

(Early morning. ZARA and CHARLIE are sneaking through the mansion.)

CHARLIE: I can't wait to hold that emerald. I bet it weighs a tonne.

ZARA: Keep your voice down, or the guards will hear us.

CHARLIE: ....

ZARA: ....

What might Zara or Charlie do that alerts the guard?

(A guard's footsteps can be heard running towards them.)

CHARLIE: ....

ZARA: (Grabs CHARLIE.) ....

How might they react to hearing the guard?

(Exit ZARA and CHARLIE.)

3 **Rewrite the extract below as a script. Use dialogue and stage directions.**

Zara and Charlie hide in a wardrobe, bickering about whose fault it is that they might be caught. Charlie insults Zara so she pushes him. He falls through a hidden door in the back of the wardrobe. It leads to an old escape tunnel.

....

....

....

....

....

....

....

Format your writing like a script.

Read back over what you've written. Is it more or less exciting than the extract it's based on?

4 Write the end of the script, in which Zara and Charlie escape from the mansion, pursued by the guard, and make it back to their hideout. Use dialogue to show what's happening.

What might Zara and Charlie do and say knowing the guard has followed them?

You could use stage directions to show how characters are speaking.

You could use Zara and Charlie's dialogue to show the guard is near.

How do Zara and Charlie get away from the guard?

(ZARA and CHARLIE follow the tunnel.)

....

....

....

....

....

....

....

....

★ **Extra Challenge**

Read back over what you've written. Mark any places where you could use dialogue or stage directions to show what's happening more clearly.

....

....

"I can show action through speech."

Answers

Pages 3-5 — Planning Your Writing

1. You should have circled the following:

Writing Idea	Purpose	Audience
1. A story about a talking teddy bear that is trying to find its way home.	Entertain	Children
2. An article from a local newspaper weighing up whether to ban cars from parking in the city centre.	Discuss	Adults
3. A leaflet from a secondary school tennis club saying why students should go to a taster session.	Persuade	Teenagers

You should have written these numbers next to the language styles:

Formal, factual language — 2

Simple, descriptive language — 1

Personal, convincing language — 3

2. Any sensible orders for the story. For example:

2, 3, 1, 4, 5, 6   2, 3, 5, 1, 4, 6   3, 5, 6, 1, 2, 4

3. Any suitable plan for the story. For example:

1. Beginning — Omar visits the jungle to hunt a rare rainbow-feathered bird.

2. Omar finds a waterfall in the jungle.

3. Omar takes a rainbow-coloured feather he finds so he can lie about killing the bird.

4. The Queen of the Jungle sees Omar leaving the waterfall.

5. Omar and the Queen of the Jungle argue over the feather and she puts a curse on him.

6. End — Omar gives the feather back and promises never to hunt again.

4. You should have circled:

Where Japan is in the world, Name of Japan's capital city.

You should have underlined:

The future of Japan, How the reader could learn more.

You should have circled:

Formal, Factual, Third Person.

5. Any suitable plan for the diary entry. For example:

Paragraph 1 — The banana boat ride and how Dad felt sick afterwards.

Paragraph 2 — All the different flavours of ice cream I ate.

Paragraph 3 — How I dug up a gold coin on the beach.

Pages 6-7 — Editing Your Work

1. You should have joined the extracts like this:

Extract 1 — Split sentences so they are easier to read.

Extract 2 — Combine sentences to help the text flow.

Extract 3 — Remove extra words.

You should have rewritten each extract, making the relevant editing change. For example:

1. 'Curling is a game played on ice. Teams push rounded stones down a lane towards a target, aiming for its centre to win points.'

2. 'There are two teams, each made up of four players, who take it in turns to slide stones.'

3. 'Each team has eight smooth, round stones. They can be used to hit the opponent's stones.'

2. Here are some parts of the extract that you could have suggested changing:

• The first two sentences could be combined and reworded to avoid the repetition of 'looked' and to give a clearer sense of what Juan is doing.

• 'Detective Juan was not scared or terrified' — 'scared' and 'terrified' are synonyms, so one can be removed.

• The last sentence could be split up to make it easier to follow.

3. Here are some parts of the extract that you could have suggested changing:

• The headline could be made more interesting, e.g. 'Hamster Hero Halts Hardware Headache'.

• The first sentence could be made more detailed to summarise what Norma the hamster did and where the incident occurred.

• The words 'grey and white' could be cut from the final paragraph to avoid repetition.

Answers

Page 8 — Proofreading Your Work

1. These are the errors you should have marked and corrected in the text:

   It was **tuff** (**tough**) being the sheriff of Hisstown. For **the** (**a**) start, Natalia hated the snakes that lurked in the grass outside of town. **the** (**The**) bright green snakes **was** (**were**) easy to spot when they slithered into town, but the pale yellow ones were sneakier. Natalia **has** (**had**) found one in her bed once. She slept outside **four** (**for**) three nights before the snake left. The memory made her shudder.

   What really made being the sheriff hard was **Ryans** (**Ryan's**) gang of bandits. **They'd had** (**They had / They'd**) held up coaches, burgled **wealfy** (**wealthy**) landowners and stolen bread from **bakery** (**the bakery / bakeries**) countless times. Annoyingly, Natalia couldn't find **there** (**their**) hideout.

   As **natalia** (**Natalia**) gazed across the fields in the warm glow of the rising **son** (**sun**), her deputy, Franklin, came running.

   "Sheriff, **I've have** (**I have / I've**) great news," he said. "I **no** (**know**) where the hideout is."

   Excellent! (**"Excellent!"**) Natalia exclaimed. "Let's get going right **away"!** (**away!"**)

Pages 9-11 — Brilliant Bats

1. 'Brilliant Bats' should be labelled as a heading. 'All Over the World' should be labelled as a subheading. 'The Arctic', 'The Antarctic' and 'Some islands' should be labelled as bullet points.

   Any suitable explanation of how the layout features make the text easier to follow. For example:

Layout feature	How it makes the text easier to follow
Subheadings	They tell you what each section of text is about.
Bullet points	They break up text to make the information easier to take in.

2. Any suitable suggestions for subheadings. For example:
   - Extract 1 — 'Bats' Diet' / 'Grub's Up' / 'What Bats Eat'
   - Extract 2 — 'Where do Bats Live?' / 'Bats' Abodes' / 'Shelter',
   - Extract 3 — 'Sleeping Habits' / 'Hanging Around' / 'Unusual Sleepers'

3. Any suitable rewriting of the text that uses bullet points. For example:

   Today, bats all over the world are at risk. This is due to a number of factors, such as:
   - destruction of their habitat
   - reduced food supply
   - disease

   You can help bats by:
   - putting up boxes in your garden for them to sleep in
   - growing plants which will attract insects for them to eat
   - joining a bat conservation group

4. You should have rewritten the text using different layout features. For example:
   - You should have given your report a heading, e.g. 'Owls in Britain'.
   - You should have used subheadings, e.g. 'Impressive Hunters' for the section of text about owls having excellent eyesight and sharp talons.
   - You should have used bullet points, e.g. to list the different species of owl or the reasons why owls are tricky to spot.

Pages 12-14 — A Day in the Life

1. You should have underlined the words in bold:

   I woke up this morning with a feeling of dread. **Our** teacher had asked everyone in the class to give a presentation. **We** had each been given a topic to talk about; **mine** was penguins. **I** hate giving presentations and birds are **my** least favourite kind of animal. Feeling sorry for **myself**, **I** trudged downstairs.

2. You should have added the words in bold:

   After breakfast, **I** set out for school alone, the nerves already building up inside **me**. As I walked through the park, I tried to comfort **myself** with the thought that **my** friend's presentation was about slugs. Surely **mine** would be more interesting than that. However, **my** thoughts were suddenly interrupted by the astonishing sight of a penguin near the swings.

3. You should have circled:

   staring, waddled, ring, entering, ran, had been

Answers

4. Any suitable rewriting of the text that uses tenses correctly. For example:

    The zookeeper **was** incredibly grateful to me for finding the penguin. I **told** him about my presentation and he **gave** me some fascinating penguin facts. I thanked him and **continued** walking to school. When I delivered my presentation, I **had** so much to talk about that I **didn't feel** nervous at all. On reflection, I am so pleased with how it **went**. I still **can't** believe what happened!

5. Your writing should be in the first person and use tenses correctly to describe your day and your emotions. Here are some techniques you should have used:

    *   The first person, using words like 'I', 'me', 'my', 'mine', 'us' and 'we'.

    *   The past tense to describe things that have already happened. For example, 'In the morning, I **met** my friends. We **were walking** through the woods when we **stumbled** upon an old tree house. It **looked** like it **had been** there for years.'

    *   The present tense to describe things that are happening now, such as your thoughts and feelings about your day. For example, 'The thought of the tree house still **makes** me excited.'

Pages 15-17 — The Life of Galileo

1. You should have ordered the topics like this:

    1. Galileo's early life
    2. Galileo's education
    3. Discoveries about space (1609-1617)
    4. Placed under house arrest by the Church (1633)
    5. Physics experiments (1638)
    6. Galileo's death

2. You should have circled:

    Initially, However, Because of this, Although

3. You should have written a paragraph about Galileo's education using linking words and phrases. For example:

    As a result, Galileo began a medical degree in 1581. **However**, whilst at university he attended a maths lecture **and** became fascinated by maths. **As a consequence**, his maths teacher, asked Galileo's father to let him study maths instead of medicine.

4. Your writing should be well-structured across two paragraphs and use the facts provided. Here are some techniques you could have used:

    *   Splitting the information into two paragraphs with a clear time, place or topic difference, e.g. information about his invention of the telescope and scientific discoveries in the first paragraph, then information about his clashes with the Church in the second.

    *   Using linking words or phrases to make the text flow, e.g. 'Based on his findings, Galileo released a book stating that the Church's theory about the solar system was wrong. **Consequently**, he was put on trial by the Church.'

    *   Using formal language suitable for a biography, e.g. 'In 1609, Galileo constructed one of the earliest telescopes.'

Pages 18-20 — Swans Storm School

1. Any suitable relative clauses. For example:

    Pupils and staff at Lastanthem Primary School in Wattleton were left stunned yesterday after ten swans charged into the school's kitchen and gobbled up the food that **was being prepared for lunch**.

    The bevy of swans, who **are well-known for harassing joggers in the park**, squeezed through a hole in the playground fence which **was due to be fixed this weekend**. The swans then dashed to the kitchen where they devoured the pizzas that **had been made as a treat for pupils**.

2. Any suitable sentences that expand the underlined noun phrases. For example:

    *   **Distraught cafeteria staff** told reporters what happened.

    *   **The aggressive swans** stormed **the tiny school kitchen**.

    *   Two of **the larger swans with sharp beaks** kept guard while the others took **the uncooked pizza from the counter**.

3. You should have arranged the first pair of sentence parts like this:

    1. The chef sneaked out of the kitchen within ten minutes of the swan invasion.

    2. Within ten minutes of the swan invasion, the chef sneaked out of the kitchen.

Answers

You should have arranged the second pair of sentence parts like this:

1. The chef alerted the headteacher after sprinting across the playground.
2. After sprinting across the playground, the chef alerted the headteacher.

4. Your writing should be clear and informative. Here are some techniques you could have used:

   - Noun phrases, e.g. '**The hungry children** were evacuated to **the top playground** to avoid danger.'
   - Relative clauses, e.g. 'The headteacher, **who has a black belt in karate**, used her skills to scare off the swans.'
   - Varied sentence structures, e.g. 'While the children watched, the swans were herded out of the school. They left through the hole in the fence, taking the pizza with them.'

Pages 21-23 — Scrimshaw's Sensational Serum

1. Any suitable examples of persuasive techniques from the extract and their effects. For example:

Technique	Example from the extract	Effect of the technique
List of three	safe to use, effortless to apply and brimming with possibilities.	Emphasises the good points of the serum.
Rhetorical question	Do you long to relive your youth? / Or know how it feels to be 80?	Encourages the reader to think about the answer.

2. Any suitable sentences that use the correct technique. For example:
   - It is an ideal gift for friends, for family or for yourself.
   - The serum is selling out faster than you can say 'Scrimshaw's Sensational Serum!'
   - You can be two, or you can be ninety-two.

3. Any suitable rewriting of the extract to make it more persuasive. For example:

   Using Scrimshaw's Serum is the best experience you will ever have. It will give you an interesting, fun and exciting break from your ordinary life. Don't you want to be able to choose your age? Then you should buy Scrimshaw's Serum and you should buy it now. It is an unbelievable product at an unbelievable price.

4. Your writing should contain various techniques to make it persuasive. For example:
   - Repetition, e.g. 'We sell all sorts of socks. Long socks, short socks, spotty socks, stripy socks!'
   - Lists of three, e.g. 'These socks are soft, warm and cosy.'
   - Rhetorical questions, e.g. 'Don't you want to give someone a present that they will love and cherish?'
   - Exaggeration, e.g. 'These stylish socks will make you a fashion icon.'

Pages 24-26 — Film of the Month

1. You should have joined the extracts like this:
   Extract 1 — Adults
   Extract 2 — Children

2. You should have circled these options:
   funniest, really good, short of money, big, Things turn funny.

3. You should have rewritten the sentences for an audience of children by using simpler language and splitting up the sentences. For example:
   - The screenwriter creates funny dialogue. For example, the two main characters use lots of silly insults and clever jokes.
   - Bryan Penholds is the actor who plays Reuben. He is in the running to win loads of acting awards.

4. You should have underlined these words and phrases:
   coolest, super-fast, good guy, fab, awesome, extra funny.

Answers

You should have rewritten the extract for an adult audience by using more complex language and longer sentences. For example:

The most enjoyable part of the film was the golf buggy chase at the end, which was made more exciting by the lively music that accompanied the main character as he weaved past golfers at top speed. The stuntman was spectacular and this made the scene very impressive.

5. You should have written a book review aimed at children or adults, using language consistent with your chosen audience. Here are some techniques you could have used:

   - A clear structure, e.g. giving a brief overview of the plot in the first paragraph, then talking about some of your favourite parts and why you enjoyed them, then discussing any aspects you think could have been improved.

   - If writing for children, straightforward language and short sentences, e.g. 'The book is about a super-smart spy. He is trying to stop his evil enemy from taking over the world.'

   - If writing for adults, complex language and longer sentences, e.g 'The spy's best friend, Jerome, is an engineer who makes numerous fascinating gadgets but has a mysterious past which he refuses to divulge.'

Pages 27-29 — The Haunted Hills

1. Any suitable description of the effect of the example. For example:

Example	Technique used	How it makes you feel
The wind was a million glass shards	Metaphor	E.g. I feel how cold and painful the wind is.
the ruins of a castle sat like a row of jagged teeth	Simile	E.g. I feel anxious because the castle sounds ominous.

2. Any suitable sentences that use the correct technique. For example:

   - Simile — Any description using 'as' or 'like', e.g. 'In the distance, I spotted clouds **as dark as coal**.'

   - Metaphor — Any sentence describing the clouds as something else, e.g. 'In the distance, the dark clouds **were a tidal wave** heading towards me.'

   - Personification — Any description that gives the clouds human qualities, e.g. 'In the distance, **angry** clouds **glowered**.'

3. You should have underlined these descriptions which appeal to the senses:

   its tangy sweetness (taste), a strong smell of smoke (smell), I heard a deep, echoing horn and the heavy march of feet (sound), cold and clammy to the touch (touch).

4. Any suitable sentences that use the correct sense. For example:

   - The sour smell of damp and mould lingered throughout the hut.

   - The stone floor was cold and hard against my body as I sat down.

   - Outside, I heard the deep rumble of a thunderstorm approaching.

5. You should have written an effective description of the setting using similes, metaphors, personification and appeals to the senses. Here are some techniques you could have used:

   - Similes to describe the landscape, e.g. 'Under the dark clouds, the shadowy forms of the mountains looked **like a huge, sleeping dragon**.'

   - Metaphors to describe the weather, e.g. 'A **curtain of rain** was blowing through the valley.'

   - Personification to describe the castle, e.g. 'The vulnerable castle **clung desperately** to the hillside.'

   - Appeals to the senses to describe the battle scene, e.g. 'The **boom of a cannon** echoed through the valley, bringing with it the **bitter scent of gunpowder**.'

Pages 30-32 — The Wizard of Whitby

1. You should have underlined these similes:

   they were like dull, grey pools, He felt as useless as a paper umbrella.

   You should have circled these metaphors:

   Wilbert's feet were heavy weights, His eyes were usually twinkling stars.

   Any suitable explanation of a simile or metaphor from the text. For example:

   - 'His eyes were usually twinkling stars' suggests that Wilbert is normally bright and lively.

   - 'He felt as useless as a paper umbrella' shows that Wilbert doesn't feel he is a good wizard because paper is a poor material for umbrellas.

Answers

2. Any suitable similes or metaphors. For example:

   Wilbert was old. His lined face was **creased parchment** and he moved as **slowly** as **cold treacle**. Achieving something unique with his magic was his desire, something that people would remember, but he felt his powers slipping away like **water through his fingers**.

3. You should have joined the sentences to the senses like this:

   Extract 1 — Smell

   Extract 2 — Touch

   Extract 3 — Taste

   Any suitable explanation of how one of these appeals to the senses makes you feel. For example:

   The horrible smell makes me feel sorry for Wilbert because it shows how bad he is at magic.

4. Any suitable appeals to the senses. For example:

   Wilbert felt **scalding** tears trickling down his cheeks and brushed them away. He heaved himself out of his chair, his joints **groaning painfully** with the effort, and trudged towards his bedroom. As he passed his owl, she gave a **soft hoot** and nestled close to him. Wilbert breathed in her **warm, dusty** scent.

5. Any suitable rewriting of the passage which uses similes, metaphors or appeals to the senses. For example:

   Wilbert pulled his warm, woollen blanket tightly around himself and fell asleep. His gentle snores became a rumbling freight train. At a sudden grinding boom from outside, his eyes shot open and he looked around like a startled rabbit.

6. You should have written an effective description of Wilbert that uses imagery and appeals to the senses. Here are some techniques you could have used:

   - Appeals to the senses to describe Wilbert's shock when he first sees the ship, e.g. 'Wilbert let out a hoarse gasp.'

   - Similes to describe how Wilbert moves, e.g. 'Wilbert rushed out of the house as though it were on fire.'

   - Metaphors to describe what Wilbert looks like when he is casting the spell, e.g. 'Wilbert was a towering pillar of concentrated power.'

Pages 33-35 — Sherbet's Sweetshop

1. You should have filled the gaps with interesting adjectives and descriptions to create a vivid picture of where the story is set. For example:

   Sherbet's Sweetshop had stood in the same spot, **between the bank and the pet shop**, for as long as anyone could remember. The walls were **a vibrant green**, and the wooden door looked as though **it was polished every day**. In the window, racks of **cream-filled** chocolates jostled for space with **sweets in all colours of the rainbow**. Every afternoon, dozens of **chattering** children gathered outside, **pressing their noses to the window** and wondering what to buy.

2. You should have rewritten the descriptive opening so it sets the scene for the reader. Here are some techniques you could have used:

   - Interesting adjectives, e.g. 'Hilda Sherbet gazed around her **bustling**, **old-fashioned** sweet shop.'

   - Similes to describe the sweets, e.g. 'The sweets glistened as brightly as stars.'

   - Metaphors to describe what Hilda can hear, e.g. 'the laughter of children was music to Hilda's ears.'

3. You should have circled the following verbs and adverbs:

   rummaged, tossing, frantically, dashed, shoved, desperately

   Any suitable rhetorical question. For example:

   What could have happened to the secret recipe?

4. You should have written an action-packed opening based on the plot outline. Here are some techniques you could have used:

   - Interesting verbs, e.g. 'Hilda **skipped** back to her shop, **clutching** her bag with both hands.'

   - Interesting adverbs, e.g. 'Ingredients for sweets bounced **wildly** in her bag as she bounded **eagerly** up to the front door.'

   - A rhetorical question to introduce a problem, e.g. 'Why hadn't Hilda's apprentice opened up yet?'

Answers

5. You should have written an opening based on the picture. Here are some techniques you could have used:

- Interesting adjectives and descriptive techniques for a descriptive opening, e.g. 'The dented and dusty toy robots were ranged along the shelf, standing to attention like soldiers.'

- Powerful verbs and adverbs for an action-packed opening, e.g. 'Henry **jerked** his head round **violently** and **stared** at the robots. There it was again: a tin leg **twitched minutely**.'

- A rhetorical question to introduce a problem, e.g. 'Who could have wound up the toy?'

Pages 36-38 — Whitebeard's Wrath

1. You should have joined the endings like this:

   Ending 1 — Clear-cut — Happy

   Ending 2 — Open — Sad

2. You should have ticked the first box and written an open ending based on it. For example:

   As the ship tilted, Whitebeard staggered and dropped the medallion.

   This was Amy's chance. As Whitebeard tried to regain his balance, she clambered up the deck towards the medallion. Another huge wave engulfed the ship. Amy and Whitebeard reached for the medallion, their fingers closing on it at the same moment.

3. Any suitable ending with a twist that the reader wouldn't see coming. For example:

   "No, you won't," Amy said confidently. "Before you stole the medallion from me, I swapped it for a golden snake."

   Whitebeard froze. He looked up slowly at his quivering hand. The angry snake hissed in his face, causing Whitebeard to stumble overboard into the dark depths of the sea.

4. You should have written an ending based on the picture. Here are some ending types you could have used and summaries of what could have happened in your endings:

- A sad, clear-cut ending, e.g. Short Jack Bronze outwits Amy to get the mythical treasure. He steals her ship, leaving her stranded on the island forever.

- An open ending, e.g. Short Jack Bronze beats Amy to the treasure, but it is cursed and he goes mad. Amy takes the treasure, but it is not clear whether she will also be cursed.

- A twist ending, e.g. The mythical treasure is in fact an illusion used to trap pirates on an island, and Amy and Short Jack Bronze have fallen for the trick.

Pages 39-41 — A Lucky Escape

1. You should have underlined:

   They're falling out of my hands, Give them here — I'll put them on the table, I'll get the floor plans, I'm going to get a snack first, I'll make notes on how to get the emerald myself.

2. Any suitable dialogue that shows action. For example:

   CHARLIE: Ouch! I just tripped over that rug.

   ZARA: And you smashed a vase, you idiot.

   (A guard's footsteps can be heard running towards them.)

   CHARLIE: Someone's coming. Help me up.

   ZARA: (Grabs CHARLIE.) We need to find somewhere to hide. Hurry!

3. Any suitable script writing that shows the events from the description. Here are some techniques you could have used:

- Stage directions to set the scene, e.g. '(ZARA and CHARLIE are hiding in a wardrobe.)'

- Dialogue that shows action, e.g. 'CHARLIE: Whoa! I've fallen into some kind of old escape tunnel.'

4. You should have written the end of the script. Here are some techniques you could have used:

- Dialogue that shows how Zara and Charlie escape, e.g. 'ZARA: We've got to keep running. The guard is right behind us.'

- Stage directions that show how the characters are speaking, e.g. 'CHARLIE: (Panting) I can't keep sprinting like this.'

- Dialogue that shows Zara and Charlie have got away, e.g. 'ZARA: I can't believe we made it back. I'm shaking like a leaf.'